Spanning the Tyne

The Building of the Tyne Bridge 1925-1929

Stafford M. Linsley

Foreword by Professor Norman McCord

Newcastle Libraries & Information Service

Newcastle Libraries & Information Service would like to thank Mott MacDonald for their generous help in the production of this book.

Most of the photographs are reproduced from a series held in the Local Studies Collection, Newcastle City Library. They were commissioned as progress records by the contractors, Dorman Long & Co. Ltd.

Exceptions are the photograph on page 8 and the back cover: reproduced courtesy of City Repro;
plates 1, 2, 3, 4, 44, 46: Newcastle Libraries & Information Service;
27: reproduced courtesy of Dr Stafford M. Linsley;
43: reproduced courtesy of Newcastle Chronicle & Journal Ltd.

Figures 1, 2 and 3 are reproduced by kind permission of the *Engineer.*

The illustration on the title page is reproduced from a commemorative booklet distributed to schoolchildren in 1928.

Cover design by A.V. Flowers.

This book was first published by Newcastle City Libraries & Arts in 1993.

Revised and expanded second edition 1998.

ISBN: 1 85795 009 7

British Library Cataloguing-in-Publication Data: a Catalogue Record for this book is available from the British Library.

Printed by Bailes the Printer, Houghton le Spring.

Front cover photograph:
The last section of the top chord of the down-stream arch is lowered into position on 23 February 1928.

Back cover photograph:
The Tyne Bridge, 1993.

About Mott MacDonald

As a world-class multi-disciplinary consultancy with a strong presence in the North East, Mott MacDonald has engineered many of the region's landmark projects. When the Tyne Bridge opened in 1928, the Group was proud of its contribution to the then largest steel arch in Britain.

Since that time, Mott MacDonald's portfolio has expanded to include such prominent schemes as the Tyne and Wear Metro and the Tyne Tunnel. Now, from offices at St Ann's Wharf on the north bank of the Tyne, it is helping shape key projects for the next century – including Newcastle's International Centre for Life and Gateshead's Regional Music Centre.

The Tyne Bridge from the Mott MacDonald Offices

Foreword

THE TYNE BRIDGE, opened by King George V on 10th October 1928, is neither the oldest nor the youngest of the bridges connecting Newcastle and Gateshead, but ever since its construction it has been one of the most potent symbols of Tyneside.

The idea of an additional high level bridge, running between Pilgrim Street, Newcastle, and Gateshead High Street, had been advocated as long ago as 1860. In 1897 Newcastle City Council had given its blessing to such a scheme, although joint discussions between the two town councils ended in failure in 1904.

The idea was taken up again in 1924 and this time agreement was reached, a success facilitated by the prospect of a hefty subsidy from central government funds for the bridge's construction. The necessary Act of Parliament received the Royal Assent on 7th August 1924, and a number of leading firms then competed for the valuable construction contract. The Tyneside firm of Armstrong Whitworth was one of the five companies which tendered, but its contract price was much higher than that of the successful bidders, the Middlesbrough firm of Dorman Long & Co. Ltd. That company was already engaged on preparations for building the much larger Sydney Harbour Bridge.

The designers of the bridge were Mott, Hay and Anderson, distinguished and experienced in the planning of large engineering projects. Their Tyne Bridge design involved a single large arch which was free to move on steel pins at the main bearings, working rather like hinges, so that the huge structure could respond adequately to such factors as variations in temperature or loading. The complex steel parts were provided by the contractor's Teesside works; their assembly was jokingly known in the area as 'the Tyne's great Meccano set'.

The bridge, the most dramatic element in the Tyneside skyline, epitomised some important historical developments. It confirmed the shift in both Newcastle and Gateshead from the old quayside area which had provided them with their original urban nucleus over a period of many centuries. It also represented the great revolution in transport brought about by the development of the internal combustion engine, and the enhanced importance of road communications. The High Level Bridge of 1849 had provided a major railway link but only a modest facility for road vehicles. The Tyne Bridge was entirely a road bridge, designed to carry not only a high density of vehicles but also individual loads up to 100 tons on four wheels.

The official opening of the Tyne Bridge was one of the great events in the history of 20th century Tyneside, and of all the structures in our region none is better known or more evocative of home to the people of our area.

Norman McCord

Building the Tyne Bridge

THE ROMANS BUILT a bridge across the Tyne, Pons Ælius, somewhere near the location of the present Tyne Bridge, but it is unlikely that this bridge survived very long after their departure. A wooden bridge seems to have been built on or near the site of the Roman bridge around the middle of the twelfth century, but it was said to have been destroyed by fire in 1248, to be replaced by a stone bridge by c.1270. The latter was the only bridge across the Tyne at Newcastle for the next 500 years, and it was only replaced after it had been largely destroyed in the great flood of 1771 (plate 1). The replacement bridge, designed by Robert Mylne, opened in 1781, and it remained the only fixed river crossing until the building of Robert Stephenson's High Level Bridge of 1849 (plate 2). By then, the Industrial Revolution was in full swing, and after centuries when only one bridge had sufficed, the number of bridges over the Tyne was about to increase quite considerably – the first Redheugh bridge of 1871, (replaced in 1901 and again in 1984), the Swing Bridge of 1876 to replace Mylne's bridge (plate 3), the King Edward railway bridge of 1906, the Tyne Bridge of 1928, and the Metro rail bridge of 1981. No Tyne bridging point between Wylam and Shields has ever been abandoned, in spite of suggestions at various times that some might be. Such suggestions have usually followed the opening of a new bridge, in the optimistic belief that the additional capacity provided by a new bridge would allow an older bridge to be abandoned.

Of the 20th century bridges across the Tyne, the most significant is probably the Tyne Bridge, Newcastle's modern-day symbol. This bridge was first proposed in 1921, by T. M. Webster, a local civil engineer, who suggested that another high level bridge was needed to augment existing road and tram crossings over the Tyne between Newcastle and Gateshead, and that it should be located near the existing High Level Bridge which was, according to Webster, 'only an old iron bridge ... never intended to carry trams in addition to the ever increasing number of cars and lorries'. The Swing Bridge was also causing problems. Closing to road traffic about 30 times every day, to allow the passage of vessels on the river, the resulting sequence of 15-minute delays to road traffic was becoming a real source of grievance (plate 4).

After continually pressing his argument for a new Tyne Bridge, the town corporations of Newcastle and Gateshead eventually accepted Webster's idea. The Tyne Improvement Commissioners necessarily became involved in the scheme, jealously guarding their control of river navigation by insisting that whatever kind of bridge was to be built, it should have no river piers, and should allow full navigational clearance across the entire width of the river, both during and after its construction. The Commissioners also insisted that no bridge-building materials were to be raised from the river during construction. As an indication of the Commissioners' general thinking on such matters, it is instructive to note that they also expressed the intention to: '... eventually ... have the Swing Bridge removed, and also to have the ... High Level Bridge rebuilt with larger spans to ease the obstruction to river traffic at this point.'

The London consulting engineers Mott, Hay & Anderson were asked to prepare an appropriate bridge design, and a Parliamentary Bill received the Royal Assent on 7 August 1924. The corporations also obtained a 65 per cent government grant towards the construction costs of the bridge, after arguing that the project would help to alleviate the chronic unemployment on parts of Tyneside. There had, of course, been some opposition to the scheme. The LNER was worried about loss of toll revenues on the High Level Bridge, and the Post Office was busy planning

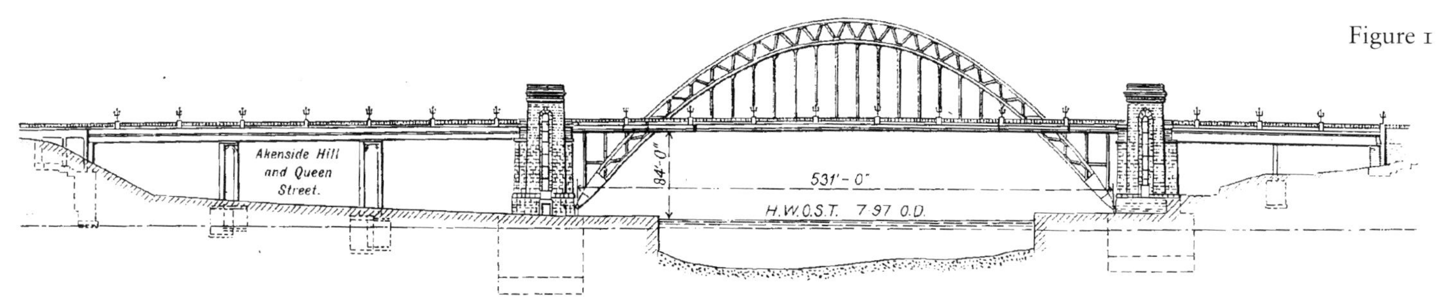

Figure 1

a new telephone exchange on the very line of the projected new bridge; both organisations eventually withdrew their objections, after agreeing terms for compensation.

After five tenders to build the bridge had been received, the lowest offer was accepted, the contract for the new bridge being let in December 1924 to Dorman, Long & Co. Ltd of Middlesbrough, with Ralph Freeman as their Consulting Engineer. The requirements of the Tyne Improvement Commissioners ensured that a fairly dramatic bridge would have to be designed, and that the manner of its construction would have to be equally bold. As it happened, a similar but much more massive task had already been commenced by the same contractors, working with the same consultant, on the other side of the world at Sydney Harbour in Australia.

Dorman Long had been awarded the Sydney Harbour project in March 1924, with a steel-arch bridge design by Freeman, derived from the Hell Gate Bridge in New York, and Mott, Hay & Anderson's Tyne Bridge design was to be patterned on that for Sydney Harbour. The Sydney Harbour bridge would be a single-span, two-hinged steel arch bridge, flanked by granite-faced pylons, with a span of 1,650 feet (503 metres), carrying a suspended deck for four rail or streetcar tracks, a roadway and pavements, at a height of 172 feet (52 metres) above the water. The Tyne bridge would be of similar design, with a span of 531 feet (161.4 metres), its road deck being 84 feet (25.5 metres) above high water mark (see figure 1).

Freeman had to develop a novel construction method for the Sydney Harbour bridge, where the deep waters of the harbour precluded the use of temporary construction supports, and this method would also have to be used for the Tyne Bridge to allow the river to remain fully navigational throughout the building contract. Work had, in fact, started on the Sydney Harbour bridge before the contract for the new Tyne Bridge was let, but the much smaller Tyne Bridge was the first to be completed.

Work on the new Tyne Bridge commenced in August 1925. Several buildings had first to be demolished, to make way for the new bridge, including five public houses – the Goat Inn, the Earl of Durham, the Ridley Arms, the Steamboat Inn, and Vinnicumbs, a Barclays Bank, the south wing of a Lloyd's Bank, a carpenter's shop, a blacksmith's shop, Ray's lodging house, an old powder mill and a pickle factory (plate 5).

Shaft sinkings and borings at the Gateshead and Newcastle sides of the bridge, enabled the depths of the known sandstone beds to be determined, and it was on these beds that the massive concrete abutments, which would take the entire thrust of the bridge arch, were founded. The thrust of the arch would be transmitted to each abutment via one foot diameter, $8^1/_2$ foot long bearing pins, resting in steel saddles which were affixed to granite block skewbacks; each granite block weighed between 5 and 8 tons, and all were brought to Newcastle by sea from Cornwall. The huge, Cornish granite-faced towers above the abutments, which are of minimal structural significance, were designed to house warehouses (never used as such) plus goods and passenger lifts; the lifts were intended to serve the quayside areas, in line with the confident but misjudged prediction, that the Swing Bridge would be done away with, once the new bridge had opened.

Concrete retaining walls, with dry filling between them, formed the land approaches on either side of the bridge. They would not be left exposed on the Newcastle side, but as the Gateshead walls would be visible, they were faced in freestone taken from the old Newcastle Gaol, then under demolition (plate 11). The bridge approach road decks, spanning between the retaining walls and the abutment towers, were to be carried on continuous steel girders, supported by pairs of octagonal steel columns, the two Newcastle pairs being skewed to accommodate existing street and building arrangements below, while the single pair supporting the Gateshead approach deck were to be in line (see figure 1).

With the retaining walls completed and temporary approach-deck support columns in place, 41½ foot sections of continuous-span decking were rolled out by hand winches, from the earth fill between the retaining walls. Each section was only rolled out as far as was necessary to allow the next section to be assembled on the dry fill, and then riveted to its neighbour. This method proved very satisfactory, alignments within five-sixteenths of an inch being maintained on the longer Newcastle spans where, at the final rolling out, some 1,600 tons of decking were moved by just four hand winches.

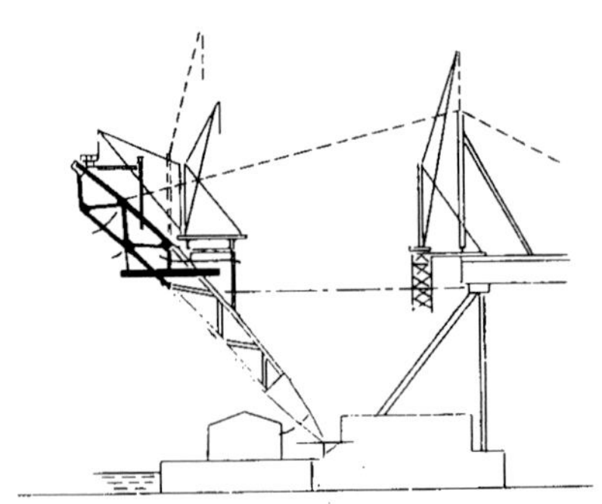

Figure 2

Since there was to be no interference with shipping during the construction of the bridge, no form of staging for the main arch could be erected from the river bed, but Freeman's method overcame this particular problem in dramatic fashion. The erection of the arch was carried out progressively from each side of the river, the method of erection used being essentially the same on both sides. Thus, with the arch bearing pins in place, the first arch rib panels were positioned by a 20 ton crane and propped up by timber falsework (plate 15). A trussed-steel cradle was then erected by a 5 ton derrick crane, mounted on a high wooden tower behind the abutments, and the same crane was then used to re-assemble the 20 ton erecting crane on cross girders over the cradle (plate 12). The 20 ton crane then handled the arch members of the second and third panels, which were supported by the cradle. With these panels in place, four wire cables were attached to the outer ends of each upper rib member, and tied back to the heads of the temporary columns supporting the approach deck (plate 16). The cradle could now be removed.

With the cables in position, the 20 ton crane was now used to erect another 5 ton crane, on the top chord of one rib. The latter crane, together with the tower-mounted derrick crane, then dismantled the 20 ton crane and its cross girders, so that they could be re-erected sufficiently further out on the arch ribs to enable the next arch panels to be assembled in place. This procedure had to be repeated, on both sides of the arch, as erection of the bridge proceeded (plates 16 to 26).

When the first set of support cables had reached their capacity, a second set was attached further out on the ribs, and tied back to masts erected on the bridge approach spans (figure 2, and plates 18 and 20). These masts were themselves tied with back-stay cables which sloped down to fixing points on the approach girders (plate 31). A jacking-post system over which the back-stay cables passed, allowed the position of the arch ribs to be adjusted during construction. The first set of cables were

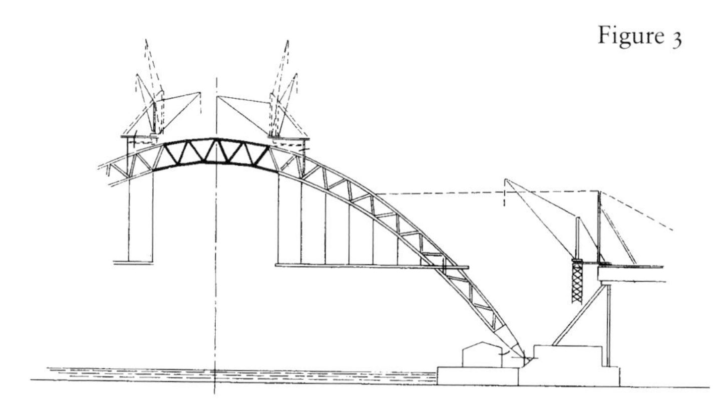
Figure 3

now removed. (Arch erection had commenced on the Gateshead side some 8 weeks before that on the Newcastle side, to enable the cradle and first sets of cables used on the Gateshead side to be transferred for similar use on the Newcastle side. The first set of cables were subsequently lengthened, to be later used for the third set of cables.)

Some bridge deck hangers and cross girders were now being put in place, and these were used to support a runway track which enabled arch members to be bogied out to within reach of the 20 ton erecting crane (plates 22, 24, and 34). As more arch members were put in place, a third set of supporting cables was positioned further out on the arch ribs, and the second set removed (plates 24 and 25). Construction continued until the last two chord members of the arch were in place, the jacking posts on the back-stay cables being lowered to close up a 9 inch gap between the upper chords and to allow the cables to slacken (figure 3 and plates 30 and 35). The arch was then fully closed. The final sets of cables were removed, and may subsequently have been re-used on the Sydney Harbour bridge, which was not completed until 1932.

The main abutment bearings for the bridge had been completed by 21 September 1927, and the arch had been closed on 25 February 1928. Progress had been remarkably rapid, as the largest single-span arch in Britain was effectively assembled within 6 months. But there was still much work to do before the bridge could be opened. The road deck plates had to be installed and covered with asphalt, concrete, and wood-block paving; ducts for gas mains, water mains, power cables and telegraph cables, had to be incorporated beneath the steel deck plates; cast-iron balustrades and lanterns supplied by MacFarlane & Co. of Glasgow had to be installed. Above all, the abutment towers had to be completed (plates 37 to 40).

In fact the Gateshead tower was not completed in time for the official opening by George V, accompanied by Queen Mary, on 10 October 1928. The opening speech by the king was recorded by Movietone News and a special radio programme was broadcast entitled 'The Bridge of Tyne: a Fantasy for Radio'. Local schoolchildren were given a day's holiday and were presented with a commemorative brochure (plates 42 to 44).

Although the new bridge had substantially increased river crossing capacity, there was unprecedented traffic chaos in the first days after its opening, as former users of the High Level Bridge deserted that route to avoid the payment of toll.

A short bibliography

Anderson, David, 'Tyne Bridge, Newcastle', Minutes of the Proceedings of the Institution of Civil Engineers, 230 (1929-30) 167-202.

'New Road Bridge between Newcastle and Gateshead', *The Engineer*, 144 (30 December 1927) 728-730, 740.

'The River Tyne Bridge, Newcastle', *Engineering*, 125 (2 March 1928) 266.

'The River Tyne Bridge, Newcastle', *Engineering*, 126 (19 October 1928) 488-489.

The Tyne Bridge, 1993,with new lighting, at the time of the Tall Ships Race .

1. The Tyne Bridge, 1772

The medieval stone bridge across the Tyne had acquired three towers and many houses and shops upon it by the 18th century. It also carried the blue stone which marked the boundary between Newcastle and the Diocese of Durham. It was very narrow in places, and with the many piers of the bridge obstructing the waterway, the force of the water through the arches was very great. On the night of 16th November 1771 heavy flooding occurred occasioned by severe rainfall in the west, and in the early hours of the morning two arches on the Gateshead side were carried away down river. An arch on the north side was driven down at about 5 o'clock. Several people lost their lives here, as did many others up and down the reaches of the Tyne.

2. The old Tyne Bridge and the High Level Bridge viewed from the Gateshead shore c.1865

A stone bridge replaced the old bridge that had been swept away in the floods of 1771. It was completed in 1781 and widened in 1801 but it was still too narrow for the increasing traffic across the river. Its 9 arches presented a great obstruction to navigation.

The High Level Bridge, designed by Robert Stephenson, was opened by the York, Newcastle & Berwick Railway Company in 1849 to provide accommodation for the increasing road and rail traffic at that time.

3. THE TYNE BRIDGES c.1890

W.G. Armstrong's hydraulically powered Swing Bridge was completed in 1876 in order to allow the passage of shipping up river. By the 1920s the often-mooted idea of building a new Tyne Bridge had become more pressing. There were constant holdups because of the frequent opening of the Swing Bridge.

Another problem was the steep gradient that traffic coming into Newcastle had to contend with. In addition, the High Level Bridge suffered from the burden of trams and slow-moving traffic. A new bridge was most desirable.

4. 2ND JUNE 1924

The Tyne without the Tyne Bridge. Traffic is held up while the Swing Bridge is open to river traffic. The time is 4.30 p.m.

5. 25th May 1925

(Above) Pilgrim Street, Newcastle, looking south. Demolition of properties 74, 75, 77-79 and 83, 84 in progress.

6. *(Right)* Pilgrim Street, looking north-west.

7. 17TH JUNE 1925

The site of the Newcastle abutment, looking north from the quayside. The two track-mounted steam cranes were used in sinking the foundations for the Newcastle abutment and tower.

8. 28TH AUGUST 1925

(Above) Hillgate and St Mary's Church looking east, showing excavations for the Gateshead abutment and temporary diversion of Hillgate. Horses and carts remove shale and ballast from near St Mary's to enable construction of the Gateshead approach road.

9. *(Right)* St Mary's Churchyard is excavated for the site of the approach road columns.

10. 18th August 1926

Laying granite setts for the Church Street diversion in Gateshead.

11. 26th April 1927

The Gateshead approach, showing the steel-trough road deck to the right with asphalt laying in progress. Behind this the retaining walls for the approach are almost complete, and faced with sandstone from Newcastle gaol, then being demolished, where they would be visible. Horses and carts are tipping dry fill between the retaining walls.

No 63
DORMAN LONG & Co LTD
No 64
9·8·27

12. 9TH AUGUST 1927

(Left) The Gateshead side erection cradle is positioned below the temporary supports for the approach road deck; this cradle enabled the lower arch members to be erected in advance of the steel cables which would eventually support the upper arch members. Work began on the Gateshead side some eight weeks earlier than the Newcastle side so that the erection cradle could be transferred across the river when its work was done at Gateshead.

(Inset left) On the same date, the bolted and riveted steel floor plates on the Newcastle approach are covered with a thin layer of asphalt and then concreted over; barrows and a man-powered tubway are the only mechanical handling devices.

13. 10TH AUGUST 1927

(Right) The Newcastle abutment under construction below the temporarily supported approach deck; the timber trestle tower supported the 5 ton derrick crane, mainly used to erect the cradle and the 20 ton erecting crane. The river lighter at the quay side has probably delivered the granite blocks from the Penrhyn quarries in Cornwall, to be used for the skew-backs for the main arch bearings; each block weighed between 5 and 8 tons.

14. 10th August 1927

A view at the Gateshead end of the bridge. The falsework deck support and the erection cradle are admired by a child with his bicycle – an immense 'Meccano Set' construction.

15. 27th September 1927

The granite skewbacks are in position within the Newcastle abutment, the steel bearing support has been affixed, and the bearing pin and first panel lengths of the arch are propped by timber falsework. The bearings were completed by 21st September 1927.

16. 27TH SEPTEMBER 1927

The arch of the bridge is taking shape on both sides of the river. The erection cradle has been removed from the Gateshead side and the lower arch members are held by four wire cables tied back to headpieces over the temporary columns supporting the approach-span girders. Masts to take support cables for the upper arch members are in place above the Gateshead road deck, and once these cables are in use, the lower cables will be transferred to the Newcastle side.

17. 20th October 1927

A view from the High Level Bridge showing the Gateshead side of the Tyne Bridge suspended by temporary tension cables. The Swing Bridge is open for the passage of ships up river.

18. 16TH DECEMBER 1927

In this snowy scene the second set of tension cables on both sides are now attached to their support masts, while back-stay cables anchor the masts themselves.

19. 30TH DECEMBER 1927

A view from the deck level on the Gateshead side. All Saints Church can be seen in the distance. Some of the vertical road-deck hangars can be clearly seen.

20. 12TH JANUARY 1928

In this general view the familiar shape of the bridge is emerging and the tension cables at the Gateshead side are in their final positions.

21. 13TH JANUARY 1928. A view from the Gateshead quay.

22. 27TH JANUARY 1928

(Above) Newcastle can just be seen in the mist through the girders of the two arches. More road-deck hangars are in place as the two sides of the arch are closing together.

23. 2ND FEBRUARY 1928

(Right) The Newcastle end of the arch, and the quayside.

24. 15TH FEBRUARY 1928

The arch is nearly complete, viewed from Sandhill.

25. 15th February 1928

A dramatic prospect of the arch from Newcastle showing the cross-bracing between the arch ribs, the construction support cables, and one of the 20 ton cranes in possibly its final position near the crown of the arch.

26 22ND FEBRUARY 1928

Lowering the last upper chord member of the Gateshead side of the arch.

27. PROBABLY LATE FEBRUARY 1928

Some of the workmen and engineers on top of the completed arches. They no doubt include Hugh Shirley Smith, design engineer, Jack Anderson, chief resident engineer, J.A.K. Hamilton, assistant resident engineer, John Holmes, plater, Henry Bird, chargehand riveter, Louis Croney, foreman fitter. The Mayor of Gateshead is centre, wearing his chain of office.

The group is standing about 170 feet above the Tyne.

28. 23rd February 1928

(Left) The last diagonal bracing is fixed to the down stream arch high above the river.

29. 13th February 1928

(Below) These workers high up on the Gateshead seem to have little safety equipment, but appear quite relaxed.

30, 31. 23rd February 1928

The two ends of the arch meet as the last section of the top chord of the downstream arch is lowered into position. The 9 inch gap was expected and the two halves of the rib were finally closed by lowering jacking posts under the backstay cables which allowed the two half arches to close together. Temporary alignment pins were then inserted between the central chord members to hold them in position.

Closure of the central lower chord members had still to be achieved and this was completed on 16th March 1928. The tall suited gentleman above, apparently with walking stick in hand, is probably J.A.K. Hamilton who devised the closing technique, later to be used at Sydney Harbour and elsewhere.

32. 2ND MARCH 1928

Backstay tension cables anchored to the approach road deck.

33. 4TH MARCH 1928

Looking down river. A cross bearer is lifted from a barge up to the bridge. It had been a condition of the contract that there should be no interference to river shipping during the erection of the arch, a condition which determined the ingenious method of construction. However, special permission was granted to raise the last six cross girders from the barge.

34. 10 March 1928

Looking north. All the hangars and cross girders are now in place.

35. 10TH MARCH 1928

A general view from the Gateshead end of the bridge. The tension cables are now slack and soon they will be removed.

36. 26th March 1928

The temporary masts and tension cables have been removed from the arch. One of the 20 ton erecting cranes has been removed and the other one will soon be dismantled but work must continue on the main towers.

37. 18th May 1928

Photographed from Sandhill, the roadway is taking shape.

38. 22ND MAY 1928

From the Gateshead side, the arch and deck hangers are completed and steel plates are being riveted into position to form the road deck. The temporary light railway, used to bring out the steel plates, was lifted as deck laying proceeded. The finished steel deck was covered with concrete and woodblock paving.

39. 17TH JULY 1928

Viewed from Gateshead, work is proceeding on the two towers. When it became obvious that the Gateshead towers would not be complete in time for the official opening, there was some talk of postponement. All the towers were designed to be used as warehouses, with five floors each, but the floorings have never been completed.

40. 27TH AUGUST 1928

The riveted steel deck of the west sidewalk; the deck plates were subsequently covered with asphalt. Both 9 foot wide sidewalks were supported on cantilever brackets. Ducts for gas and water mains, power and Post Office cables were run beneath the steel plates.

41. 6th September 1928

Viewed from the north side, the arch is complete. Work is proceeding on the Newcastle towers while the Gateshead backstay mast is being dismantled.

42. 10TH OCTOBER 1928

The Tyne Bridge on opening day, with the Gateshead towers not yet finished. Note the bunting on the Swing Bridge. The formal reception party greet the King and Queen.

43. 10th October 1928

The procession reaches the Gateshead end of the Tyne Bridge.

44. 10TH OCTOBER 1928

King George V and Queen Mary preside over the opening ceremony. The Lord Mayor of Newcastle, Stephen Easten, is to the right of the King. The Mayor of Gateshead is to the left of Queen Mary amongst the many dignitaries.

45. 27TH MARCH 1929

The Tyne Bridge finally completed, viewed from the High Level Bridge with the Swing Bridge in the foreground. The architectural features of the abutment towers were designed by R. Burns Dick of Newcastle.

46. 13TH JULY 1929

The Tyne Bridge in use.